The Big Bat

Written by
Anne Jewell

Illustrated by
Tony Waters

BUTLER BOOKS

Published in the United States of America

Printed in Canada
Manufactured by Friesens Corporation in
Altona, MB, Canada in March 2010
Job # 53640

First Printing: March 2010

ISBN: 978-1-935497-14-1

Published by:
Butler Books
P.O. Box 7311
Louisville, Kentucky 40207
(502) 897-9393
(502) 897-9797 (fax)
www.butlerbooks.com

Designed by:
Bisig Impact Group
640 South 4th St.; Suite 300
Louisville, Kentucky 40202
(502) 583-0333
www.bisig.com

To learn more about Louisville Slugger Museum & Factory, visit
www.sluggermuseum.com or swing by the World's Biggest Bat
at 800 West Main Street, Louisville, Kentucky, 40202.

Edward Paul Reed
4 months
15 lb. 15 oz.
26" tall

For Joseph

"Wow! It's humongous!"

When Katie saw the World's Biggest Baseball Bat, she wanted to take a picture of it.

Katie planned to be a fabulous photographer when she grew up.

"It won't even fit in the picture," she said. "It's so tall!"

The Big Bat is 120 feet tall.

That's as tall as seven giraffes,

180 double-dip   ice cream cones,

or 24,960 pennies.

Katie's little brother, Ace, planned to be a
stupendous superhero when he grew up.

He even wore a spiffy cape that
day to Louisville Slugger
Museum & Factory.

Ace wanted to help his sister.

"I will move the Big Bat," he said, "so you can get a better picture of it."

But the Big Bat is too heavy to move, even for a stupendous superhero with a spiffy cape.

The Big Bat weighs 68,000 pounds.

That's the same weight as
five tyrannosaurs,

540 jockeys,

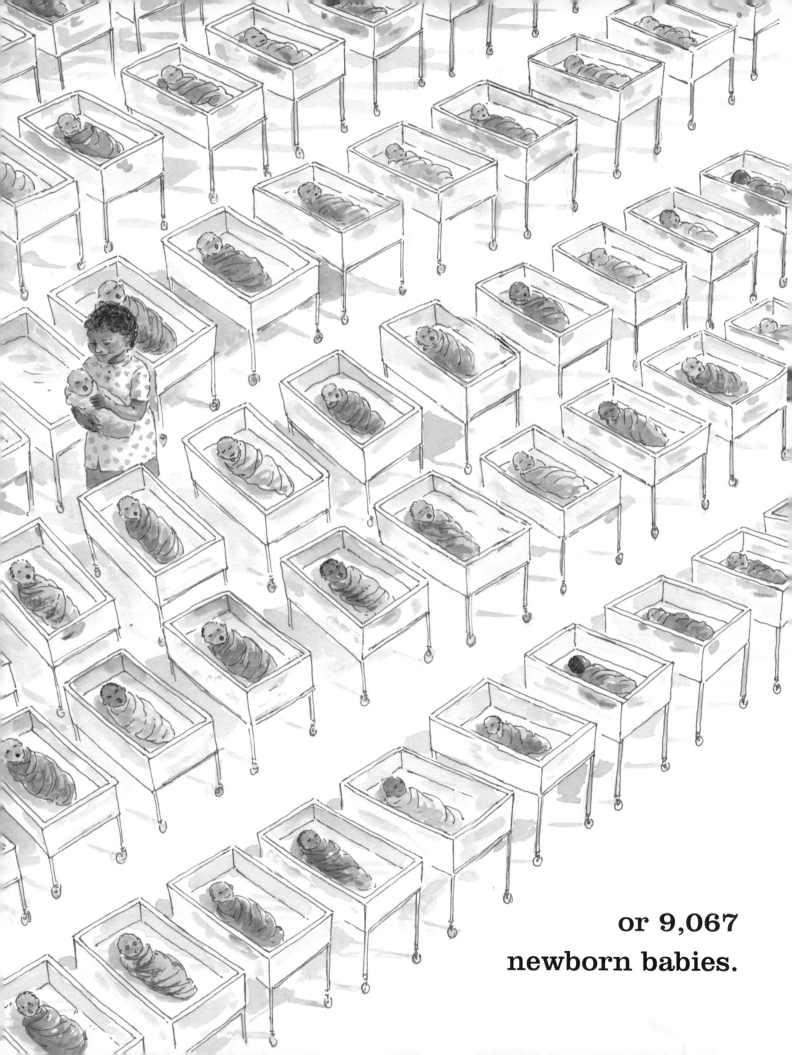

or 9,067
newborn babies.

The Big Bat is tall, heavy, and hollow.

"Hollow" means there is nothing inside of it.

A balloon would float from the bottom to the top.

Many things could fit inside the Big Bat.

The Big Bat could hold eight
dump trucks of jellybeans,

2,667 wagons of crayons,

or 30,000 gallons of lemonade.

"I'm thirsty," Ace said.

He sat down to conserve his
superhero strength.

"That's it!" Katie said.

She got down on the ground next to her little brother and pointed her camera up at the World's Biggest Baseball Bat.

Now, it fit in the picture!

Katie took a fabulous photo.

After that, Katie and Ace each had humongous glasses of lemonade.

And Katie thanked Ace for his help.

Math can sure be a lot of fun!
Here is the math we used for this zany story:

Big Bat Height = 120 feet or 1,440 inches:

1 Giraffe = 17 feet
17 feet x **7** = 119 feet
www.learnanimals.com

1 Ice Cream Cone = 8 inches
8 inches x **180** = 1,440 inches
www.thecomfycow.com

208 Pennies = 1 foot
208 pennies x 120 feet = **24,960** pennies
www.ainsedu.org

Big Bat Weight = 68,000 pounds:

1 T-Rex = 13,000 pounds
13,000 pounds x **5**.231 = 68,003 pounds
www.buzzle.com

1 Jockey = 126 pounds
126 pounds x **540** = 68,040 pounds
www.factmonster.com

1 Newborn = 7.5 pounds
7.5 pounds x **9,067** = 68,003 pounds
www.whattoexpect.com

Big Bat Volume = 4,000 cubic feet:

1 Dump Truck = 500 cubic feet of jelly beans
500 cubic feet x **8** = 4,000 cubic feet
www.dumptrucks.com

1 Wagon = 1.5 cubic feet of crayons
1.5 cubic feet x **2,667** = 4,001 cubic feet
www.redwagons.com

7.5 Gallons = 1 cubic foot
7.5 gallons x 4,000 = **30,000** gallons
www.wikianswers.com

Remember, you can do different things with numbers. What if the dump trucks we used were smaller? What if the heap of crayons in each wagon was bigger? You can think of your own fun ways to measure the Big Bat!

The Big Bat

The World's Biggest Bat is an exact-scale replica of Babe Ruth's 34-inch R43 Model Louisville Slugger bat. Made of ASTM A36 carbon steel, it is hand-painted to look like wood. The signature on the bat belongs to Bud Hillerich, the man who made the company's first bat in 1884. Over 200,000 guests visit Louisville Slugger Museum & Factory every year, where they can marvel at the Big Bat, tour the factory where Louisville Slugger bats are made, explore interactive galleries and admire awe-inspiring baseball memorabilia.

About the Author

Anne Jewell is the Executive Director of Louisville Slugger Museum & Factory. She grew up in Toledo Mud Hens territory, and still has the first Louisville Slugger softball bat her father gave her when she was in the fourth grade, a wooden 39-65 model. Anne was particularly pleased with the deep red bat, because it looked so good with her red and blue uniform. She has also authored *Legendary Lady: The Story of the Belle of Louisville*, and *Baseball in Louisville*. This is her first children's book. Anne roots for the New York Yankees, but admits to a soft spot for the Chicago Cubs.

About the Illustrator

Tony Waters has been drawing ever since he first scribbled pictures on the wall beside his crib. Working full time for an architecture firm as a renderer and model builder, he has also illustrated a number of children's magazines and books, including three of his own. The illustrations for this book were done in pen-and-ink and watercolor on Strathmore 140 lb. watercolor paper. A native of Charleston, South Carolina, Tony goes to "The Joe" stadium to stomp and shout for the local minor league team, the Charleston RiverDogs.

And, for those of you keeping score at home:

Katie is named for the "baseball mad" heroine in the lesser-known lyrics of a very famous song. She's the gal who originally asked her beau to "Take Me Out to the Ballgame."

Ace is a term used to designate the top pitching talent on a baseball team. Years ago, "ace" also meant "run scored" in baseball.